A FORTRESS BOOK

FAITH AND HEALTH

by

Kristofer Hagen

MUHLENBERG • PHILADELPHIA

Printed in U.S.A.   UB2007

FOREWORD

The need for putting what we, as Christians, believe into words everybody can readily understand poses a constant challenge. In response to that challenge the New Testament itself was written in a language commonly spoken and understood. Through the ages handbooks, catechisms, and tracts have been written and, since the invention of printing, published to meet the need for clarifying in every age what it means to be a Christian.

Whether it is more difficult to be a Christian in one age than another is hard to say. But being a Christian in the second half of the twentieth century is becoming more and more complicated. This heightens the challenge of spelling out for our day in an uncomplicated way what it means to be a Christian. To put the thought patterns of theology into terms that are readily understood is not easy. Yet saying what we believe in such a way that others, without too much difficulty, will understand what we are talking about is the test of our own grasp of what we believe and hold to be true.

In tackling this task the authors of Fortress Books do not try to make a difficult faith seem easy but to make it easier for the reader to see how demanding Christian discipleship really is and how important it is for him to give meaning to what he believes in what he does. And so the authors want to give the reader clues to guide him in making his decisions from day to day. It is the hope of the publishers that these small books, dealing with central themes of Christian faith and life, may succeed in their purpose.

Helmut T. Lehmann
Editor

PREFACE

Any book worth reading on a subject so personal as faith and health must come out of the crucible of human experience. While it is not for me to claim that these pages are worth reading, it is my duty to point out that the human experience from which these ideas are drawn includes many people. My parents, teachers, parishioners, patients, colleagues, and friends have all played a large though vaguely defined part in formulating the opinions herein expressed. It would be unfair not to mention them.

We should also recognize that the constant expansion of medical knowledge may make some ideas herein stated subject to revision as further knowledge unfolds. This is particularly true in the fields related to emotionally induced illnesses.

Special thanks are due to Dr. Donald Simonson, the Rev. William Gentz, and Mrs. Hagen for valuable suggestions and inspiration. Miss Marjorie Cords' efficient typing of the manuscript was much appreciated.

Kristofer Hagen, M.D.

Mohulpahari, India
August 8, 1960

CONTENTS

ix

INTRODUCTION

Vital religious faith is the most important single thing in a man's personal health. There are moments when only the right medicine or surgery or nursing care can rescue him from disaster due to disease or injury. There are also times when properly chosen X-ray therapy, physical therapy, shock therapy, or other intervention with his bodily processes can preserve health or prolong life. But by and large, year in and year out, a man's relationship with his God and with his fellowmen makes a bigger difference in his enjoyment of health than do all the achievements of modern medical science. In his daily, personal walk with God man finds a confident faith in the goodness of the universe, a glowing relationship with other people, and an optimistic courage for the uncharted future that sustain him in better physical condition than if he has none of these things. Like a properly tuned-up motor his body works better because he is "adjusted" internally by his Creator.

Indeed, as every doctor knows, the right medicine or surgery or nursing care may fail to cure some people of their disease because they lack a vital religious faith. There are medical situations in which properly chosen therapy may fail because the individual is not in touch with God or is not living on the right basis with his fellow-men. At such times prayers can be more important than pills; faith may do more than physiotherapy; confessions may accomplish what injections could never do.

The purpose of these pages is not to discount the miracles of modern medicine. They are a welcome gift from God. Has not God created and inspired the human intelligence that has discovered these miracles? As science advances, however, we want to be sure that man does not lose an important essential in his personal health —his faith and trust in God. Doctors cannot accomplish the greatest good for the patient unless his faith is aroused to the point where it opens the way for God's healing grace to flow into him.

SIN AND DISEASE

Before proceeding with our discussion of the relation between faith and health we should perhaps say a word about sin and disease. Doctors and ministers are often asked whether illness is a punishment for sin or not. The question is not put as directly today as it was by Jesus' disciples. Confronted with a man born blind, they asked Jesus, "Who sinned, this man or his parents, that he was born blind?" Most people raise the question in a more oblique way.

Medically speaking, one has to say, "Yes, sin does cause disease, but not always." Some sins always cause disease, some sins often do, some never do. Some diseases are always caused by sin, some diseases may be, and some diseases are almost never caused by sin. The sins that cause disease may produce damaged tissue in a person, in others near him, or in others far from him. If there were no sin there probably would be no disease.

Yet we have to admit that for some diseases we have so far discovered no cause for which man could be held morally responsible. Research may change the picture as developments unfold. When a disease is traced to a preventable cause it becomes the moral duty of man to avoid that cause.

A few illustrations may help to clarify the relationship between sin and disease.

S.K., age 29, a young, single woman, at least sixty pounds overweight, obviously short of breath, wondered if she were low in thyroid. Her metabolism tests were normal, her blood pressure was high. She was advised to reduce for the benefit of her health. One day at breakfast with friends the subject came up again, but she jokingly said, "If I can't eat I don't want to live. Please pass the bacon!"

When this woman gets a stroke or develops hypertensive heart disease prematurely in her thirties or forties it is clear that her undisciplined eating will be the cause. Such lack of discipline is sin.

Mrs. M.G., age 34, mother of four children, came in one day complaining of heart palpitations, upset stomach, lack of appetite, weight loss. Physical examination, blood tests, X-rays were all negative. Finally, after several attempts at defining and treating her ailments, the real cause was revealed. From her lips came the sad story of an unfaithful husband who refused to leave the "other woman." The patient was beside herself with fear that her home would be broken up and was desperately trying to do her best to salvage the family. Her anxiety caused her symptoms.

It is easy to see in this case how the husband's sin caused the wife's illness. Medical offices have countless records of a similar nature, cases in which one person's sin causes disease in another person. When it proves impossible, as in the above case, to remove the offending sin, the ill person may have to seek God's help in developing the stamina to withstand the emotional stress without further damage to his own health.

J.B., aged 31, a businessman, saw his doctor because of feeling weak and tired and "sick all over." He also had a low-grade fever. Examination revealed heavy bronchitis and sinusitis, a very rapid heart that was weakened due to pericarditis, and an enlarged and tender liver. Closer questioning revealed that he was in the habit of taking several drinks "to relax" every evening and that as a result his diet had suffered. Analysis of his case showed that his resistance to infection had been reduced by a poorly functioning liver so that he could not fight off the streptococci in his throat and nose. The chronic infection in his sinuses and bronchi began to damage his heart sac or pericardium, again because his liver was too weak to manufacture the antibodies that resist disease.

In this case the alcoholic habits were damaging his liver. Decades of research have now proved conclusively that alcohol has deleterious effects on liver metabolism in patients whose livers have been previously damaged by hepatitis or other adverse conditions. Treatment for this man meant using a combination of antibiotics, high vitamin diet, and cessation of alcohol consumption. Since he felt that he needed "something to relax" at the end of the day, carrying out the third part of the treatment was not easy. He had to think out his basic life problems and resolve his tensions without the use of chemical relaxants. In other words, he needed a relaxing faith in God. Seeing the full implications of such a cure through takes months and years. A whole new set of habit patterns is needed requiring a persistence only God can give. The man is presently working out his problem under the guidance of his pastor.

Sometimes the sin that causes an illness is not so easy to trace. It may be some error of judgment which is really not sin in any personal or moral sense. It may be some human mistake being made by civilized mankind in innocent ignorance of its consequences. There are, for example, quite a number of cases of epilepsy that have been traced to a bleaching agent which was used for many years in white flour. Once the link with epilepsy was established it became, of course, morally and soon legally wrong to continue using it. The medical profession has been guilty of its share of such "mistakes." It would be wrong to call any of these disease-producing mistakes of mankind sin, since they were not intentional or due to negligence. More disciplined thinking and working on the part of the whole scientific team may prevent repetitions of such costly mistakes in the future.

FAITH IN YOUR GOD

For I will restore health unto thee, and I will heal thee of thy wounds, saith the Lord.—Jeremiah 30:17.

God wants all men to be in that relationship with himself and with other men wherein they can claim his promise of restoration and healing in Jer. 30:17. Maximum health is God's goal for man not only for man's own good but also for the kingdom's good. As we used to say in the Army, "A sick soldier cannot fight," or on the mission field, "A sick missionary cannot evangelize," so also we can say in the local church, "A sick parishioner cannot do his best for the kingdom of God." This is not strictly true in every case, for as we all know, God sometimes miraculously uses a "bruised reed," but generally speaking we must surely agree that God wants his workers to be as strong and healthy as possible.

There are people who are inclined to blame God for their illnesses and ask, "Why did God send this affliction on me?" God does not *send* afflictions. He may *permit* them to occur in keeping with the due processes of natural law. He is a health-giving God.

A good example of the health-giving nature of God is seen in the New Testament account of how Jesus, known as the Great Physician, healed a man who had been paralyzed for thirty-eight years.[1] The exact nature of his ailment is not clear. One might interpret his in-

[1] John 5:2-9.

7

validism as a psychosomatic illness in which some original pathology had led to a state of psychological inertia. Jesus aroused his dormant will to get well, a prerequisite of any cure, by asking the man, "Do you *want* to be healed?" His challenge reminds one of Seneca's dictum, "It is part of the cure to wish to be cured." The invalid's excuses about having no one to help him into the miraculous pool of Bethzatha when the angel stirred it up reveals an unhealthy, over dependent type of personality. Jesus miraculously changed this by asking the man to take up his pallet and walk. The man promptly did as he was told. Thus the Master Healer changed a sickly, discouraged, and over dependent invalid into a healthy, optimistic, and active individual. The miracle was as much psychological as physical. Faith in Christ made a new man out of the patient.

In medical practice doctors are repeatedly impressed with the good health of the godly and also often depressed by the rapid physical decline of the ungodly. This is not to say that godliness always produces health or ungodliness always produces disease. Rather, the godly conquer disease and its effects more readily.

The ability of godly people to "take it" when illness does strike is a fact known to most doctors. Their wholesome attitude of co-operation with treatment, their cheerful optimism in battling through an illness or operation, their patient tolerance of pain and discomfort are a daily inspiration to the practicing physician. No words may be exchanged with the doctor directly on the subject of their religious faith—yet in the background of the treatment situation the doctor often feels the steadying and healing influence of their faith.

The opposite is also a common experience in medical practice. People who completely lack faith in God or whose faith is only a superficial church-going have very little ability to "take it." They frequently insist that the doctor hurry up and get them over this "d—n thing" so they can resume their daily pattern of living. They are angry at the interruption of their usual routine, and they are afraid of the dire possibilities in their illness. A few bold exceptions to this rule are no proof that it is generally untrue.

What is it about faith in God that promotes physical health? We may summarize our explanations under four headings.

The first healthy effect of a living personal faith in God is the *forgiveness of personal sin and guilt*. This results in a good conscience and aids in producing restful sleep, harmonious digestion, a stable nervous system, peace of mind—all very important requirements for health. Every day in any doctor's office you can meet patients who would pay dearly for any one of these things. There are, of course, pills and medications designed to produce them temporarily, but only a good conscience can produce them permanently. There is no pill that will give man a good conscience. This is strictly God's business.

M.J., aged 29, had an active peptic ulcer that gave him pain and sleepless nights. While undergoing medical management by diet, antacids, and tablets, he told the doctor of a long standing, burning resentment against his immediate superior at work. The resentment gave way only slowly to a combined approach in which several people, including the patient's pastor, helped him to face his superior at work and clear up the causes for the resentment in honest conferences. When this was accomplished the ulcer healed up and no further symptoms developed.

A second fruit of faith in God is a *life of good, moral habits that promote health.* Christian people are not prone to the so-called "harmless little vices." The absence of excessive tobacco use, late night entertainment, alcoholic habits, gambling, and the like in an average Christian's life helps to protect health and prolong life. Most insurance companies pay close attention to the absence or presence of these habits in an applicant, and it is no secret that Christian people of good, moral habits enjoy preferred risk rates for the simple reason that they are healthier.

T.C., age 36, a traveling salesman, was gambling and drinking enough to undermine not only the happiness of his home but also the state of his health. His nervous system, liver, and digestive tract all showed unmistakable evidence of premature deterioration. The church reached him with its message, he came "back to God" where he had been as a boy and became an active church member. The physical improvement was dramatic. He visits his doctor now only for annual check-ups which show a healthy, normal male.

A third quality of life that comes from faith in God is a *basic happiness and satisfaction in the home and community life of the individual.* Married people live longer than single people and happily married people live longer than unhappily married ones. Years of medical practice have taught me that whenever a home is about to break up due to internal disharmony or dissension, medical problems of one sort or another multiply in its wake—ulcers, hypertension, colitis, insomnia, nervousness, weakness, injuries, accidents, etc. The opposite is also true. With some Christian families about all we have to treat them for is the routine immunizations of their children and maternity care as the children come. Happiness and optimism beget health. As an ancient scriptural proverb says, "A cheerful heart is a good medicine, but a downcast spirit dries up the bones." [2]

M.Y., age 38, a bus driver, came in with vague, abdominal pains. Laboratory and X-ray studies were negative. In due time it was revealed that he was carrying on an affair with a woman other than his wife. There were numerous office calls thereafter to care for his troubles, his wife's troubles, and the children's troubles, all directly or indirectly related to his unhappy home situation. Divorce is pending. The outlook is not bright for robust health for any of them.

A fourth health-giving result of faith in God is *emotional stability and tranquillity*. This "shock absorber" quality enables a person to withstand the natural shocks of life—the unexpected accident, the sudden serious illness, the loss of fortune, destruction by fire or tornado. Invariably, the easiest patients to handle in such periods of catastrophe are the ones who practice a genuine faith in God. They come through the episode with the least amount of stress diseases or breakdowns, because, as

[2] Prov. 17:22.

E. Stanley Jones once said, "A Christian is a person who can be happy, regardless of what happens to him."

> L.J., age 67, a coronary heart patient, lost her son in a terrible accident. Her grief was assuaged by her sustaining faith in God so that a minimum of sedation was necessary to tide her over and minimize the strain on her heart. She is doing well.

It would not be correct to imply that all Christian people are perfectly healthy personalities. One needs to work only a few weeks in a doctor's office to find a goodly number of neurotic, frustrated, poorly adjusted people among church members. Many of them, of course, may be poor Christians in that their church affiliation is a mere formality. How much worse they would be without their church affiliation is hard to say. The church, by its shepherding role in the lives of people, should attract a lot of dependent, inadequate personalities into its fold. That the church has not managed to do a perfect job with them is no evidence against the value of a vital faith in God. It is rather a challenge to the church to apply its message to such human souls with more precision and care. But the overall effect is plain. These people are immeasurably better able to cope with their health problems because of their faith in God.

WHAT IS FAITH?

Since we are finding faith in God so important to good health, let us try to define what we mean by it. Like many other phrases in common usage the full meaning of the words may not be as apparent as it might seem.

To believe in God is, of course, to believe that God exists and that the attributes usually assigned to him are true, namely that he is Creator of the universe, almighty, all-knowing, everywhere present. However, it is entirely possible to give a sort of intellectual assent to these verities and yet not have faith in God. *Faith is a relationship that comes as a result of experiencing God.*

Just as the trust and confidence a child has in his parents is built on repeated experiences of receiving love and care from this source, so also our faith in our heavenly Father is a result of experiencing his love and care. Faith of this kind is not so much an act of man's will as a result of man's experience with God.

Thus we have to agree with the theologians who insist that faith is not an accomplishment of man himself. It is rather a gift from God that gradually grows in an individual as he opens his heart to God's grace and discovers over the years that God is good, kind, helpful, true, dependable. This is why the faith of people who have lived a number of years in conscious fellowship with God is usually stronger and more durable than the faith of a new believer.

Doubt and unbelief are not simply the absence of faith. They are usually the symptoms of a person caught in a struggle, a struggle between the forces of good and the forces of evil. Such a person would like to believe in God's goodness, knows full well that he should believe in God's goodness, but because he is enmeshed in some selfish sin, he perverts his underlying faith into defiant doubt or unbelief.

No one can live in this world without experiencing some of God's goodness and grace. The truest response to this experience is to believe more and more in God. The only reason some people respond with disbelief is sin.

Just as a child is healthiest when parents and children live together in mutual respect and love, in ever-deepening trust and confidence, so the children of God are healthiest when they look gratefully and honestly to him with growing confidence in his wonderful ways with men. Such personal confidence, born of experience, is faith.

FAITH IN YOUR DOCTOR

He cures most in whom most are confident.—Galen.

When a person goes to see a doctor he wants very much to have faith in him. The development of a spirit of honesty and confidence between patient and doctor is essential to successful healing. The relationship is just as important to the doctor as it is to the patient. Each must believe in the other. The doctor cannot make a dependable diagnosis or outline proper treatment unless the patient has openly and honestly told him all the facts in his story of how the illness started and developed. The patient cannot carry out the doctor's orders faithfully unless he believes in the doctor and feels that the doctor has dealt with him honestly and wisely.

Faith in the doctor is no substitute for faith in God. The doctor is not God. He may aspire, as all conscientious people do, to become an instrument of God, but it is a mistake to expect of him out-and-out miracles of cure or prognosis. Both the patient and the doctor are, after all, human, and have to rely on the healing forces of nature to accomplish the actual inner work of tissue repair. As doctors often say to their patients, "We doctors really do not heal anyone. God heals you. We only try to help you into a proper pattern of life so that nature and your faith can make you well."

Faith in the doctor is no repudiation of one's faith in God. It is simply faith in those means which God has provided for man's healing. Some people seem to feel apologetic to God for going to a doctor. They act as if they had called first on God to heal them and since he did not seem to be doing the job they decided to go to a doctor. They feel almost guilty in going to anyone as human or secular as a doctor. This seems like a foolish confusion of issues. Common sense dictates that God expects us to make full use of the means he has provided, that is, the medicines, medical and surgical skills, and hospitals available to us. In many of the New Testament miracles involving health problems the sick people Jesus confronted were often startled by being asked to do something for themselves. Jesus expected them to make full use of even the primitive means open to them in their day. One can only conclude that a person really has no right to ask God for help in his illness until he has made a sincere effort in good faith to use all available human medical means.

The first step in developing faith in your doctor is to choose him wisely in the first place. This choice now faces about one family in five every year, since up to 20 per cent of all people in our country move to a new location within one calendar year. In due time these families find themselves "looking for a good family doctor." As pointed out by the American Medical Association, a good family doctor can take care of 85 per cent of the average family's ailments himself and can best advise the family on which specialist to consult for more complicated problems. The training of family doctors is being improved constantly. The American Academy of General Practice insists on at least fifty hours of postgraduate refresher courses or medical society meetings a year as a requirement for continuing membership.

Measures of this kind aimed at improving standards of medical care have perhaps by now eliminated all or nearly all of those ill-qualified doctors Sir William Osler had in mind when he complained in 1895: "Such a doctor, without physiology and chemistry, flounders along in an aimless fashion never able to gain any accurate conception of disease, practicing a sort of popgun pharmacy, hitting now the malady and again the patient, he himself not knowing which." [1]

In choosing a family doctor a person should, then, try to get one who is well trained and who co-operates with the various organizations trying to keep him up-to-date. The selection may be made easier by getting information from the local county medical society. Beyond that, for more personal advice on which doctor to choose, most people ask friends, neighbors, ministers, druggists, and others to help them. This usually results in a happy choice that seldom requires changing.

A second step in developing faith in your doctor is to give him your full co-operation. A doctor is human enough to feel quite keenly the response he arouses in the patient. If the patient has shown good faith in reporting his symptoms as accurately as he can, his doctor usually responds by listening attentively, writing down the story, and proceeding to examine the patient carefully to start working toward a diagnosis. A harmonious interplay of the patient's willingness to reveal and the doctor's eagerness to probe usually works best. Patients

[1] Harvey Cushing, *The Life of Sir William Osler* (London: Oxford and the Clarendon Press, 1925), I, 408.

17

who conceal important facts from the doctor or stubbornly stick to their own ideas of what is wrong with them or of how to cure their condition may test the doctor's patience to the point where he cannot do his best. From then on teamwork between patient and doctor may fail.

Having said all this, I must add that one has to use common sense. As one patient said, "You have to watch out for these doctors—they may order too many tests or prescribe more drugs than are good for you." This may, indeed, be perfectly true at times, and it is a wise patient who is honest and courageous enough to say so to his doctor when he feels that things are going too far. If there are tests or drugs the patient cannot afford or tolerate, he has a perfect right to tell the doctor. The doctor may still insist that they are necessary, but it should be remembered that the healing situation thrives on a free and easy relationship between patient and doctor. The co-operation the patient gives his doctor should not be blindly subservient. Most laymen today are fairly intelligent on health matters and under their doctor's supervision can often make valuable suggestions for the investigation or treatment of their disease. The old autocratic idea that the doctor is always right has disappeared along with the black, ministerial garb of yesteryear's medico.

A third suggestion for developing faith in your doctor is not to expect too much of him. The advent of modern "miracle drugs," of fantastically successful plastic and reconstructive surgery, of constantly newer and greater achievements in heart and brain surgery has led some people to expect the impossible from their doctors. If a head-on collision on the highway mangles a patient's face and body, it is expecting too much that the result should always be cosmetically perfect and functionally as good as before. If a serious disease strikes, it is expecting too much that the doctor have the patient up and walking around in a few days. If a dread disease like cancer or multiple sclerosis occurs, it is expecting too much that the doctor produce a complete cure.

The practice of medicine has become a perilous occupation economically. Larger and larger lawsuits against doctors for supposed malpractice have made some doctors wish they had never started practice. Many of these suits are based on the fact that the patient or his relatives expected too much of the doctor. As long as doctors are human they can never be perfect. We have a right to expect them honestly to maintain high standards of competence or, in other words, to do the best that can be done. But the best is sometimes not good enough to save a patient in this imperfect world. Every doctor knows this and for this reason he can never guarantee results. He can only guarantee that he will do his very best. The patient and his relatives have to be willing to share the risks of practicing medicine with their doctor to this extent. If the results are not perfect and the doctor has done his best, we can only remember that life is full of uncertainties.

Before leaving this subject a word should be said about seeking consultations in difficult cases. Whenever the patient or his relatives feel that the doctor is facing a problem more difficult or complicated than a man of his training can solve, they should feel free to suggest calling in a consultant. The doctor normally suggests

19

this first, but if he does not do so, for one reason or another, it is perfectly all right for the patient or his relatives to suggest it. In the present state of medical history it is manifestly impossible for any one man to know everything in medicine and for this reason there are now over seventy different specialty groups, able representatives of which stand ready to co-operate in medical teamwork on the more difficult cases.

A fourth step in developing faith in your doctor is to believe that God can and does work through him to cure you. This is true whether your doctor is a personal Christian or not. The doctor's own destiny will be decided by his own faith and life, but it will not affect yours. Most doctors have a vital, religious faith and many are active members of the church. Even those who have no personal faith are usually men of integrity who respect life and death and know the value of a human personality. However, the doctor's personal faith, like that of any free American citizen, is really his own private affair. As Montaigne said in the sixteenth century: "It can be of no importance to me of what religion my physician or lawyer is. This consideration has nothing in common with the offices of friendship which they owe me." [2] In the use of healing forces in the world God is not limited to the services of those personally dedicated to him. The Bible is full of illustrations of how God used the services of undedicated, stubborn, and stiff-necked people to accomplish his purposes.

For this reason it seems a sign of immaturity or insecurity in people when they insist on going to a Christian doctor—as if he could heal them faster or better.

[2] Montaigne (1533-1592), in his essay, *Of Friendship*.

They act as if such a doctor had an inside track with God and thus could better direct the healing forces of nature. This is just as foolish as to say that a Christian farmer will have better success at farming than a non-Christian farmer of equally intelligent and industrious approach. No, God permits his sun to shine on the just and the unjust, the same rain falls on the fields of the good and of the indifferent. The same laws of nature apply to all, regardless of the church to which they belong or do not belong. In medicine the same laws hold for the non-Christian doctor as for the Christian. What a confused chaos life would be if there were no dependable laws of nature! These laws of nature in medicine and surgery are simply statements of the way things work, as observed by scientific minds over generations of investigation. The doctor who best understands these principles and uses them in treating his patients gets the best results, regardless of his religious views.

FAITH AND HEALTH IN CHILDREN

I the Lord your God am a jealous God, visiting the iniquity of the fathers upon the children to the third and the fourth generation of those who hate me; but showing steadfast love to thousands of those who love me and keep my commandments.—Exodus 20:5-6.

The health of a child is a precious thing, the most precious physical possession a child has. It can be a fleeting thing—here today and gone tomorrow. It may be an irreplaceable thing—offering no chance for a second attempt at cure. It may also be an elastic thing—stretching miraculously around a biological impasse that would be impossible for an adult. At times it is an expensive thing—redeemed from disaster only by delicate surgery or costly medicines. Usually it is an emotional thing—touching parents and other adults to tears or sympathy.

No wonder then that millions of dollars and millions of man-hours have been spent in medical research to safeguard the health of children. With all the effort spent on the conquest of such childhood diseases as polio, diphtheria, meningitis, rheumatic fever, congenital heart defects, and the like it is disturbing to note that on the spiritual front some parents do a poor job keeping their children healthy. Vaccines, antibiotics, and vitamins flow into children much more freely than faith, hope, and love, without which no child can be really well.

J.B., age 12, received a constant parade of injections

and high-priced medications for treatment of severe asthmatic attacks. A thin, nervous, neglected child, he early felt rejected by his parents who always seemed too busy with their own activities to give him the love and attention he craved and needed. In his adjustment to a "hard and unloving world" he is already manifesting the internal crying which psychiatrists say is the emotional basis for much asthma.

While glaring emotional-deficiency diseases like this case are rare, many parents today have difficulty in producing that quality of spiritual atmosphere in the home which is conducive to maximum health for their children.

Nothing shows up true faith in God or lack of faith in God as clearly as having a sick child on your hands. I have seen parents become so panicky and frightened by the slightest symptom in a child that the patient is made much more ill than he really is. I have seen other children calmly accept serious illness or even life-long defects with equanimity because the parents had an unshakable faith in the goodness of God.

Piety can, however, go too far. In dealing with the very sick child prompt action may at times be far more important than prayer. Parents who turn an emergency like acute croupy bronchitis (acute laryngo-tracheo-bronchitis) over to God without seeking proper medical attention may be losing precious hours in which life could be saved. They have expected God to do what they should have done themselves.

Conversely, parents who fuss and fret around a sick child who has had the help called for may interfere with God's healing processes by their lack of faith. When the best available medical help has been given to a sick child he should be surrounded with an atmosphere of calm, confident belief in God's healing power and allowed to get well in peace.

The role of parental faith in the healing of a child is well illustrated in the way Jesus healed a nobleman's son at Capernaum.[1] The nobleman loved his son greatly and no doubt had done all that could be done with the medical measures available to him, but the child's life hung precariously in the balance, threatened by a fever. We surmise the fever may have been pneumonia, typhoid, malaria, or some similar disease. When the father went to Jesus in faith, the son's illness passed a crisis and he began to recover at the precise hour when the father's faith met up with Jesus' power. Any sick child whose parent has done the best that can be done medically and adds to that an open faith in God will be greatly benefited by that faith. In a critical illness it can spell the difference between failure and success.

The importance of confident faith for the healing of a child is well shown in the use of antibiotics to cure infections. Family doctors and pediatricians are constantly besieged with telephone calls and visits from parents who want Johnny's bad cold treated with a "shot of penicillin" or a "prescription for an antibiotic." While every doctor has to develop his own criteria for the use of antibiotics, the question often boils down to a struggle between the parents' insecurity and the doctor's patience. Insecure parents all too often wind up with a problem like this one:

K.D., age 4, seemed to have no resistance to infec-

[1] John 4:46-53.

tions. Since early infancy every little infection had been treated with penicillin or tetracycline or some other antibiotic, because various doctors had repeatedly yielded to pressure from the parents to "do something." Infections occurred repeatedly all winter long with few or no well periods in between. The parents finally began to wonder if they should even take the youngster out at all in the winter because of the danger of infections. He became a "hothouse plant" with no opportunity to develop natural resistance to the world's bacteria-filled environment.

While every such case deserves a careful evaluation from the standpoint of allergy and other inherent physical defects, there is no doubt in the mind of any practicing physician that most such cases follow a typical pattern. Nature's own effective antibody mechanism against disease has not been given a chance to work in such children because antibiotics have been overused in response to pressure from the parents who believe too much in modern medicine and not enough in God and his natural healing processes. A child should be given a chance to fight off some of the milder infections of life by himself, perhaps with the assistance of an aspirin or two, plenty of fluids, and rest. If he is blessed with parents who believe enough in such a program to stick to it and rely on the healing mechanism implanted by God a much healthier youngster develops than if he is coddled by antibiotics through every little cold.

This oversimplification of a difficult problem in medical practice today may be so easily misconstrued and taken in the wrong way that I must advise any parent who is concerned about this to talk frankly with his child's doctor about it. Sometimes deep-seated parental personality problems, guilt feelings, or other psychological maladjustments may underly the situation and may even call for psychiatric help. More often, some simple common sense faith in God and in nature's healing process will remedy the situation.

Emotional weakness or immaturity in parents can unwittingly cause a disease pattern in the child. Enuresis (bed-wetting), a condition estimated to afflict as many as 15 per cent of all children over three years of age, is often a result of some such parental deficiencies.

O.L., age 9, was brought to the doctor for help in his problem of enuresis. Physical examination and urinalysis were normal. Questioning revealed that the boy's father had been away from home in military service from the boy's birth until he was over two years of age. The father, on his return from the Navy, got involved with "another woman" and nearly broke up the home. This resulted in serious emotional insecurity for the boy just at the time when bladder control would have been developing. In time the marital triangle was straightened out, but the father-son relationship remained so disturbed that the boy's enuresis persisted. Scolding and firm attempts at correction of the "foul habit" failed. When the father was taught to accept his child more completely and love the boy more adequately, a little help was given with mild drug therapy and the boy's enuresis stopped.

Many health problems in children are the indirect result of poor disciplining by parents. Disobedient children are more prone to accidents, colds, infections, and a dozen other ailments than are obedient children.

J.W., age 11, was brought in because of mental confusion following a twenty-foot fall from a building under construction. He had entered the building and climbed up on it in direct disobedience to warning signs on the building and to his mother's explicit instructions to stay away from there. Miraculously enough, no fractures were evident on X-ray and the cerebral concussion was mild, yielding promptly to therapy. Past history revealed that he had always been accident prone. His overly strict, religious mother had been consistently unable to enforce discipline, partly because the boy's father had shiftless, alcoholic habits and was inclined to let the boy have his way.

Disagreement between parents about discipline increases a child's difficulties in learning to obey. It is the duty of parents to find a common spiritual basis for rearing their children. We have no right to insist that parents rear their children in any particular version of the Christian faith. But we do have a right to expect that parents who agree to beget children physically should also agree to rear these children spiritually and should apply rules of conduct to their children in keeping with some common spiritual ideal.

All this is to say that good parental example and warm parental love are just as important to a child's health as good diet and medicine.

FAITH AND HEALTH IN
ADOLESCENTS

For everything there is a season . . . —Ecclesiastes 3:1.

Youngsters in their teens and early twenties are generally pretty healthy. They seldom see a doctor. When they do get sick, they are often greatly concerned. Even when the illness is minor, the worry in the youngster's mind can be major. An active, personal faith in God often opens the door to new vistas of health for the youth who is troubled with such problems. Young hearts, like young tissues, heal quickly.

Skin problems, such as acne and other blemishes, while never posing a serious threat to a young person's existence, often affect his personality development in a serious way. Many a teen-ager feels so ashamed of his complexion that he slips by degrees into an introvert shell of self-pity and seeks gratification in dangerous daydreaming. Whoever can help such a young person to believe firmly in God's goodness, to work actively for the improvement of his future while struggling patiently with his skin problem, will have been a vast boon to that youngster. Medical science today can offer only a partial cure for adolescent skin problems. Time relieves most of the trouble; very little acne persists far into the twenties. The teen-age skin patient is aided most by the inner confidence that comes from a personal faith in God who forgives, who loves and supports and guides a young man on his way.

Rheumatic fever, with its threat of serious heart damage, is one of the most trying health problems faced by young people in our climate. Modern intensive treatment of streptococcic sore throats has helped eliminate a lot of this disease, but it still afflicts thousands of teenagers annually. Aside from the damage done by bacteria in such cases, just as much harm may be done by fear as by other elements in the situation.

> J.P., age 20, had been bedridden with rheumatic fever and rheumatic heart disease since the illness had forced her to quit high school in her senior year. Fear, engendered partly by her own feelings of inferiority, had reduced her to a thin, pale, waxy looking invalid with no future. Careful cardiac evaluation by a competent heart clinic established her potential; emotional rehabilitation helped her find again a working faith in God, in life, and in her future. She got up from her bed, took a business course, and is happily employed today. Faith displaced fear and salvaged a rheumatic heart patient.

Few situations call for as careful a combination of medical and spiritual management as does rheumatic fever in a young person. The most frequent mistake is to let an overdose of fear cancel out the healing forces of nature. Faith in God and in a wise medical regimen for controlled activity help the patient the most.

Health problems related to sex can be vexing to adolescents and their parents. While the actual incidence of sex deviations is no doubt overrated by the much misunderstood Kinsey reports and other similar reports, the fact remains that every doctor's consultation room yields some tragic case histories in this line.

M.B., age 15, was greatly relieved to learn from his doctor that neither his nocturnal emissions (wet-dreams) nor his masturbation had ruined his future. He was thereafter quite willing to seek and accept God's forgiveness in his life as a whole and co-operate in directing his interests toward healthy sports and social activities with mixed groups.

The illegitimately pregnant teen-age girl is a difficult problem, calling for a rare combination of faith, hope, and charity in all who deal with her. By breaking openly with the established and accepted Judeo-Christian standard of chastity she has usually lost status with the group and rendered herself so destitute emotionally that she needs expert handling. Her problem is a bit too complicated for us to discuss here. The prevention of such sex catastrophes to teen-age girls is in our domain, however. We had better work harder on prevention than we have in the past, since teen-age illegitimate pregnancies have doubled in the last fifteen years. There are almost two hundred thousand illegitimate pregnancies a year in the United States.

Studies show that the surest way for a girl to "stay out of trouble" is not only to know the facts about sex but also to develop a solid Christian personality through faith in God. When a girl has this from her church life and her parents' example it provides an almost unbeatable combination for keeping her out of the reach of preying "wolves."

You may notice that I said "almost" unbeatable. Every

once in awhile one sees a girl with the best Christian family background get into trouble. We may try to explain such inconsistencies by saying, "This is the way life is," and leave it at that. But in dealing with these "best family backgrounds" doctors often run into indications of serious trouble between parents, for example, or unreasonable strictness in the family's code of conduct. In such situations we may find the youngster rebelling early and heading toward trouble. They only demonstrate again that a child's first need is for love.

The surest family relationships are based on honesty and faith. Parents who do an honest job of trying to rear their children right in the first twelve to fourteen years of life and develop with their children an open, sincere understanding of each other may expect the youngster to get through the teens unscathed. During those teens, while the youth is often rebellious and straining for more and more independence, it is most important that the parents believe in the youngster and say so, plainly and repeatedly.

To put it another way, it is most important that the parent believes in the truth implanted in the young heart during the first twelve to fourteen years of life and in the ability of the Holy Spirit to work in the hearts of the young. It is sheer self-centered arrogance the way some parents won't trust their teen-agers out of their sight—as if to say that only they can guide them through the conflicting emotions of adolescence. As I often say to parents overly worried about their teen-agers, "You just have to outline simple, carefully planned rules for them to follow and otherwise leave them pretty much alone. You must believe that what you have done before this will bear fruit in decent and acceptable behavior in your son or daughter now."

The one thing that has destroyed teen-age girls from good homes more than anything else is lack of faith—parents not believing in their children. Redemptive faith in actual practice is not only a relationship between a human being and a divine being. It is also a relationship between two human beings.

Youthful tensions can lead to *gastro-intestinal disturbances* of greater or lesser degree, sometimes even to active peptic ulcers. The story may vary, but frequently a frustrated striving for success that the youngster cannot quite achieve causes the tension. Overly ambitious parents may have led the youth to adopt goals beyond his capacity. When failure threatens, whether it be in school or in a job, troubles commence.

Ulcerative colitis in a teen-ager is often the result of deep-seated inner tensions and resentment. Dr. Moench reports such a case:

"M.G.B., a quiet, unfriendly boy, the youngest of the family, dominated by an aggressive, demanding mother, left home to attend college. . . . In his second year he met a girl who looked and acted quite like his mother. She pursued him and began to make him feel obligated to marry her. He resented many of her aggressions, but was unable to free himself. He then met another girl in whom he found the qualities he liked. . . . He fell in love with her and decided to terminate his relations with the first girl. While he tried to muster enough courage to tell the first girl, he began to have numerous, loose, bloody stools and was admitted to the hospital where a diagnosis of ulcerative colitis was made. The internist became aware of the conflict and refused visiting privileges. The diarrhea promptly subsided. M's mother came to visit him and the diarrhea recurred. She was sent home and the patient improved promptly. The first girl eluded the reception desk and the nurses and visited him. In the next 24 hours he had 17 stools."

As Dr. Moench so strikingly concludes, "The diarrhea may represent a hostile act, the patient saying with his colon what he is unable to verbalize." [1]

Certainly, tensions and resentments in young people can best be resolved in an atmosphere of independent, mature, personal confidence in God. The child who has been steered in the direction of such a faith during his early years will have the best chance of maturing into such a healthy relationship with God in his teens.

FIVE THINGS TO DO

The church's part in developing personal qualities in young people that will improve adolescent health may be summarized in these five points:

1. Accept the adolescent on growing terms—by confirmation, church membership, and the like. He is very sensitive to disapproval and scolding criticism. Accept him for what he is and where he is and let him grow up in the church and to adult stature.

2. Provide group activity and therapy, including a

[1] Louis G. Moench, *Office Psychiatry* (Chicago: Year Bk. Pubs., Inc., 1952), pp. 88-89.

frank facing of sex, family relationships, and choice of vocation. Give him plenty of chance to try his wings at leadership and program participation.

3. Forgive his mistakes and failures and introduce him to the forgiving Savior who says, "Neither do I condemn thee, go and sin no more."

4. Release his emotional tensions creatively in worship, confession, discussion, the sacrament of the altar.

5. Awaken his affection and extend his loyalties to the world-wide program of the church. Enlarge his horizons by introducing him to the challenge of missions, foreign, home, social, charitable.

FAITH AND HEALTH IN
ACTIVE ADULT YEARS

*He who has health has hope and he who has hope has
everything.—Arabian proverb.*

The common, chronic diseases of life's middle years are
diseases of frustration, fear, and fretting. Their prevention and cure are more spiritual than physical. Thus
they differ from such acute emergency diseases as appendicitis, pneumonia, injuries, and infections which nowa-
days receive pretty standardized organic treatment. In
their treatment faith plays only a supporting role. With
such stubborn diseases as peptic ulcer, high blood pressure, obesity, nervous disorders, and bowel disturbances,
however, treatment is more involved.

MEN

Suburbia today is full of men with ulcers. They may
be hard-driving, eager, successful men by day with rising
incomes in their businesses, but they also turn and toss
restlessly at night with rising acid titres in their stomachs.
The underlying frustration may vary from case to case,
but often it is the old game of office politics and an
unpredictable boss who hands out promotions according to no reasonable pattern. The man on the way up
the ladder of success is more likely to have ulcers than
the man at the top. As one boss roared, "I don't get

37

ulcers, I give 'em." If the second or third man on the "totem pole" could only speak out and tell the top man what he thinks of his policies he would burn with less resentment and develop less acid in his stomach.

Repressed anger is a common cause for ulcers. To help such people, someone in Denmark opened a place where for a few cents a throw you can hurl pieces of chinaware against a cement wall, thus giving vent to the suppressed feelings. The idea has some merit; it is at least a half-cure.

Another common emotional pattern underlying an ulcer-tendency is fear of failure in a new position.

J.Z., age 36, consulted his physician because of burning pains in the pit of his stomach and under the right shoulder blade. The pains were worst in the late afternoon and at night, often robbing him of sleep. X-ray studies showed a duodenal ulcer crater. History revealed that two months earlier he had been promoted to a divisional superintendency, a position in which he felt insecure and afraid of failure. After determining that his promotion had apparently not exceeded his actual ability, a program of developing his self-confidence and renewing his fundamental faith in God was instituted. In this program his pastor played a very helpful role. Bland diet, antacids, and the emotional rehabilitation produced a lasting cure in a few weeks.

A lasting cure? Perhaps. Experience teaches a doctor that such a patient may do well only until the next crisis, the next promotion, or the next reshuffling of personnel in the firm. Sometimes a doctor is confronted with a person who is inadequate for the promotion and has to be advised to retrench to a less responsible position. Usually, however, the patient is capable and only needs to find his way through to victorious faith in God that forms a sound basis for practical faith in himself. Strangely, genuine self-confidence is based on faith in God and his completely adequate love for man. All other self-confidence is a sham which time exposes and destroys.

WOMEN

A common diagnostic duo seen on the charts of patients in their middle decades is "Obesity and Hypertension." The two conditions do not always go hand-in-hand, but they generally do. We often promise our overweight patients with high blood pressure, "We can almost guarantee that for every pound of weight you lose, you will lose one point in your blood pressure." When a thirty-six-year-old housewife weighing one hundred ninety pounds walks into the office we are not surprised to find her systolic blood pressure about one hundred ninety millimeters of mercury. The solution to her headaches and nosebleeds and general nervousness may not be simply a reducing diet and some headache pills, however. The doctor is confronted with the fundamental problem of why she got so fat in the first place. If this problem is not solved, her initial determination to lose weight and lower her blood pressure will dwindle and fade after the first glow of success. Reducing pills are worse than useless in her case.

M.B., age 39, housewife, mother of five children, saw her doctor because of shortness of breath, lightheadedness, sudden spells of weakness, and heart palpitations of about four weeks' duration. Her height was 64 inches, weight 198 pounds, blood pressure 210 systolic and 130 diastolic. Electrocardiograms revealed a fundamentally sound heart with minor changes. A history of some twinges of pain in her right upper abdomen led to gall bladder X-rays that showed stones. She was a lonely wife who saw her husband seldom because he was too busy with his work. Her loneliness sought satisfaction in overeating.

This is an all-too-familiar case history in suburbia today. The woman is tied to her child-rearing job twenty-four hours a day, seven days a week, emotionally satisfied only in a hit-and-miss fashion by a husband who is too busy out in the world making a living and achieving "status" for himself and his family. She is emotionally starved. Hungry for love and attention from people of her own age group, she finds too little of it in life as it is and so seeks it in the easy substitute of food.

Such people have stomachs that have never forgotten a lesson learned at mother's breast. Love and food are intermingled in an infant's experience so inextricably that later in life when the going is rough and a person is shortchanged on love, he seeks substitute satisfaction in food. Food is a handy and plentiful substitute in America today.

The experiences described usually come at a time in life when the husband is more successful, money is more plentiful, the foods one always wanted but could never afford are now easily obtained, so the wife eats. It would not be so bad if she only got fat. The trouble is she gets fat and hypertensive and full of gallstones and other troubles.

It is idle to tell such women that what they need is more faith in God. They need it all right, and in a very practical way. They and their husbands need to learn that faith in God means also faith in each other and time for each other. Such a husband needs to co-operate in baby-sitting so his wife can get out and associate with other people her own age. He needs to take his wife out once in a while so that she remembers that he loves her. He needs, in other words, to demonstrate his faith in God by having more love and time for his wife and family.

This leads me to emphasize a very important observation made recently by a Swiss psychiatrist, Dr. C. G. Jung. He points out that modern, intelligent women are often frustrated by the relatively inferior status assigned to them in life. Though they may be college-educated, they still find themselves known only as Mrs. Somebody-or-Other and tied to the obscure chore of raising several youngsters. This 168-hour-a-week job ties them down so much that they feel like a sort of free household servant to their husbands. In this monotonous drudgery, they fail to keep any individuality of their own. They need individuation, that is, activities and interests of their own that are worthwhile, constructive, important in the world's work today.

This is, of course, the underlying psychological reason for the existence of such important organizations as Women's Guilds, Women's Clubs, League of Women Voters, and other volunteer service organizations for women. Women today need to express their individualities in constructive enterprises or else they get fat, care-less, hypertensive, and full of gallstones. They may get that way anyhow, but not so readily. Here, as in other phases of a family health program, one needs faith in action, a faith in God that expresses itself in the action of doing good among men in the world.

NERVOUS PEOPLE

Nervous disorders are such a common and pressing health problem in active, adult Americans that the last two or three years have witnessed a fantastic traffic in tranquilizers. Tranquilizing drugs may at times serve a useful purpose in calming down a temporarily nervous heart, a chronically upset stomach, or a trembling hand, but as a permanent answer to the many cases of "nerves" that stream through doctors' offices daily they are totally inadequate. Their dangers are obvious—they may destroy all ambition and initiative, they may blunt the intelligence so that the patient cannot solve his underlying problem, they may produce troublesome and toxic side-reactions.

What, then, is the poor patient to do? He should co-operate with his doctor in trying to find, under God's enlightening help, the causes for his nervousness and proceed to revise his living habits to eliminate those causes.

> T.K., age 39, housewife, came to the doctor's office with rather severe abdominal pains, crampy in nature, unrelated to any certain foods or time of day. The pains often kept her awake at night. She com-

plained of "too much gas on her stomach," lack of appetite, some weight loss. She was obviously too thin and had the pallor of a borderline anemia. Convinced that she had a cancer in her digestive tract it was hard to prove to her that X-rays showed a normal gastro-intestinal tract. As the history unfolded under treatment, her fears regarding her four children, three of whom were troublesome teenagers, became more apparent. She improved only when tranquilizers gave way to a rehabilitation of her faith in God and in her children's future under God. The change took months to accomplish. Fortunately, her church had an active youth program that helped guide her teen-agers aright.

The most common causes for "nerves" in the patients who come for help are frustrations of the normal urges of life—the urge to succeed in life, the urge to socialize with one's equals, the urge to marry and to mate happily with one's spouse, the urge to communicate with one's Maker. Unless these four goals are achieved with some measure of success the nervous system begins to show signs of stress. We cannot achieve these without believing in God enough to let him show us the way.

FAITH AND HEALTH IN
DECLINING YEARS

*He who would pass the declining years of his life with
honor and comfort, should when young, consider that he
may one day become old, and remember, when he is old,
that he has once been young.—Addison.*

The most essential ingredient for health in old age is
faith—faith in the goodness of the universe, faith in the
sure fruits of past years, faith in the brighter hopes of
future years, faith in the value of human energy even
to the last ounce, faith in a God who has work for every
man to do until he needs him on earth no longer, faith
in a shining life beyond the grave. Even casual contact
with older people convinces me that a great difference
exists between those who have faith and those who do
not. There are old people and old people.

Some oldsters are unhappy, unhealthy, cantankerous
cranks. Others are beaming benefactors until their dying
day. What makes the difference? Vitamins, hormones,
food supplements? Only in part. The difference lies
more in the mental and spiritual attitude of the oldster.
Faith, hope, and love enhance life and improve health
as long as the heart beats. Their lack blights life increas-
ingly until life is gone.

Let me explain the importance of faith beyond sixty
under four headings—the importance of faith to bones,
arteries, digestion, and nervous system.

1. *Bones.* As age advances bones often become weak, porous, decalcified, ready to crumple at the slightest injury or to snap at the merest fall. The aging person may even lose an inch of two in height because of the gradual reduction in the bodies of the spinal vertebrae or in the length of other bones. This condition, technically known as osteoporosis, leads to curvature of the spine. While certain new hormone combinations may halt or delay it, prevention is accomplished best by an active life, an active faith in God, the Giver of life. Faith in God and his plan for one's life helps a man to stand straighter, eat better, look taller, carry his shoulders more erect. All these habits of a lifetime exert a healthy influence on the skeleton.

Mrs. C.D., age 76, had a rather far advanced case of curvature of the spine due to osteoporosis. She began to think her life was over and lost her desire to live. Her doctor gave her a combination hormone tablet that helped some, but under the inspiration of her church she gained a renewed faith in God and his plan for her sunset years that was worth far more than the hormone tablets. She is a ray of sunshine today to all her grandchildren, and her bones have stopped shrinking.

2. *Arteries.* The old adage, "You are as old as your arteries," could well be amplified with, "Your arteries are as weak as your faith," because a fresh and vigorous faith in life somehow or other helps keep arteries young and fresh. Hardening of the arteries, thrombosis of the arteries, rupture of the arteries—all these are real and dangerous threats to old people. They may spell invalidism, amputation, death.

Arterial degeneration is certainly related to the dietary habits of a person's early and middle years. We now believe that plain diets, low in cholesterol-rich foods, low in hard fats, are definitely beneficial to the arteries. It may take another decade or two before these facts are all definitely understood and taught to people generally. Meantime, one thing is clear—a youthful attitude and spirit help immeasurably to keep the arteries elastic and open. An active spirit helps keep the body active, and this prolongs life by keeping the walls of the arteries supple.

On Harriet Beecher Stowe's seventieth birthday, Oliver Wendell Holmes said, "To be seventy years young is sometimes far more cheerful and hopeful than to be forty years old." Oldsters can stay young by maintaining a vital interest in younger people and their doings. Old age is a disease which is at least partially preventable. The faith needed trusts implicitly that God would not keep a person here on earth unless he had some work for him to do. Sometimes that work is simply to help guide and inspire the young.

3. *Digestion.* A common cause of premature aging is faulty nutrition. Many old people let their eating habits deteriorate into a routine of coffee and bread or rolls. They forget that a balanced diet is important throughout the whole of life, beyond sixty as well as before sixty. Proteins (meat, milk, eggs, or cheese) and vitamins (fruit and vegetables) are fundamental, daily requirements for bodily health and may be omitted only at the risk of losing out in the stream of life just when it should be the most gratifying.

The causes for the poor eating habits of older folks

vary. Bad teeth, poverty, poor cooking arrangements, digestive disorders, lonesomeness—these are the common excuses given. Sometimes old people lose their zest for life entirely and commit slow suicide by refusing to eat anything at all. Depression and discouragement at "being shelved" may underlie most of their dietary troubles.

Optimism, faith, and courage are essential if a man is going to continue to eat well beyond seventy years of age. These personal qualities cannot be given to older people by anyone else, by government agencies or pension plans. Necessary as it may be for government and other agencies to care for older people, especially in their final weeks, it always makes me unhappy to hear a plea for "doing something for our senior citizens." They are perfectly capable of doing something for themselves if given half a chance! They have lived a long time and have learned in this world that people do not thrive or grow on having things done for them.

The healthiest and best-eating older people I have known are those who continue active and useful in some aspect of life as long as they possibly can, often long after the usual retirement age. Such activity in the declining years is sparked by a faith in God, in God's need for a man's services until he calls him from this world.

4. *Nerves.* One of the hardest effects of aging for people to understand is the effect on the nervous system, on the way people think and act. Old people may undergo rather marked personality changes as the process of arteriosclerosis takes its toll in the brain and other parts of the nervous system. Some previously calm and

collected individuals may become nervous, trembling, fearful, weak, emotional. Alertness of response, sharpness of memory, quickness of perception may fade rather rapidly away and leave a dull, disoriented, confused, and unco-operative individual.

At first glance this may sound like a result of aging over which we have no control. After all, if the arteries clog up and the brain cells die for lack of blood supply, what can we do about that? Unless God works a miracle and produces new arteries and new brain cells, isn't the outlook hopeless? In reply to that, may I say first that we need not expect God to work a fantastic miracle of reversing the natural aging process to believe that his plan for us will preserve our nerves in a useful state for longer than otherwise.

Most doctors are quick to admit that such subtle influences as the will to live, an ambition to finish an important job, a great desire to see some loved one, and other psychological forces may add many good days and even years to the life of a nervous system. Simeon's experience[1] in finding that his eagerness to see the promised Messiah helped him to live long enough to hold Jesus in his arms is a phenomenon that medical men have seen repeated time and time again. Such eagerness of faith has a beneficial effect on the nervous system.

The opposite of this is certainly a common medical observation. Many a person's brain and nervous system have been seen to decline from the day some dear relative died or the day some great disappointment came into that person's life. Discouragement, defeat, and doubt

[1] Luke 2:25-35.

lead to rapid deterioration of a nervous system. Anticipation, aspiration, and activity give extra life to a nervous system that is nearing the end.

The presence or absence of a vital faith in a person beyond fifty may make a difference in how early he should be retired. The arbitrary retirement age of sixty-five in most organizations is an unrealistic one. It fails to recognize the indisputable fact that some people's nervous systems may be showing marked deterioration at fifty-five while others may be capable of excellent work at seventy-five.

The time will probably come in our society when objective tests of efficiency, rather than calendar age, will be used to decide when a man should retire, taper off his responsibilities, quit driving a car, etc. In any case, the time will never come when a man's spirit will fail to affect the rate at which his nervous system declines. Optimistic faith in God benefits a man to his dying day.

FAITH AND
PSYCHOSOMATIC DISEASES

*May the God of peace himself sanctify you wholly; and
may your spirit and soul and body be kept sound . . .*
—1 Thessalonians 5:23.

The church has long recognized a fact which the medical
press has only recently emphasized, namely that full
health necessarily involves the interaction of body, mind,
and soul, that all medicine is, in a sense, psychosomatic.
This new emphasis has led many doctors to shed their
old philosophies of dualism or pluralism, in favor of a
somewhat monistic view of man, one in which mind
and body and perhaps even the soul are considered
inseparably one. Aside from such philosophical background thoughts, the practical fact is clear—a doctor
does not get far in treating just the body or its organs.
He must treat the whole man, whatever the illness. Even
in a case of a fractured leg, it is his job not just to cure
the broken leg, but to cure a man with a broken leg.

Psychosomatic medicine is thus simply "a return to
the ancient art of looking at the patient as an ill person
rather than as a collection of malfunctioning organs." [1]
Some of the best men in the field think that the term
"psychosomatic" is misleading and suggests a non-
existent dualism. They urge that one should rather speak
of "holistic" or "comprehensive" medicine.[2]

[1] Moench, *Office Psychiatry*, p. 56.
[2] Henry H. W. Miles, Stanley Cobb, and Harley C. Shands,
Case Histories in Psychosomatic Medicine (New York: W. W.
Norton & Co., 1952).

Since W. B. Cannon in 1915 started modern psychosomatic medicine with his book, *Bodily Changes in Pain, Hunger, Fear and Rage,* this branch of medicine has progressed rapidly to encompass, explain, and explode a host of illnesses which have afflicted mankind for centuries. Recent progress in this field is no less spectacular and no less helpful to suffering mankind than the wonder drugs and antibiotics.

Before proceeding to the part one's religious faith may play in curing or preventing psychosomatic ailments, let us get a few basic facts clear.

1. *Psychosomatic ailments are very common.* Of the patients who seek medical help in the average doctor's office, anywhere from one-third to two-thirds of them have been classified as having psychogenic ailments in the sense that the root cause of their complaints is some sort of psychological or spiritual stress. However, to attribute all disease for which no organic cause is found to some vague emotional conflict is careless medicine. Not all ailments can be passed off as psychogenic just because they lack organic findings by present diagnostic methods. One must at least demonstrate or identify the stressful situation.

2. *Psychosomatic ailments are real, not imaginary.* It is a serious tactical and factual mistake for a doctor to say to a patient, "It's all in your imagination" or "in your head." His headache hurts, his asthma wheezes, his ulcer bleeds, his heart pounds.

3. *Psychosomatic ailments are largely honest ailments.* Such patients are seldom if ever malingerers. There are some psychiatrists who insist that there is no such thing as true malingering. While those of us who have been

in military medicine doubt this, we surely can agree that people with psychogenic complaints are honest, law-abiding, respected citizens whose emotional stress has evolved unconsciously and unwittingly into genuine bodily illnesses or malfunctions.

4. *Psychosomatic ailments are most common in middle-class people.* The very rich and the very poor are likely to resolve their conflicts by misconduct such as drinking, fighting, reckless driving, or adultery. Misconduct of this kind often leads to head injuries, fractures, alcoholism, venereal disease. The well-to-do may also try to solve their problems by travel or hazardous recreation. In the middle classes, however, suppression and repression, unrealistic goals, religious and community disapproval, social and economic climbing—such conflicts lead to inner tensions which cause migraine headaches, ulcers, colitis, eczema, cardiac disturbances—all predominantly middle-class diseases.

A few case histories may illustrate how faith can serve to prevent or cure diseases of this kind.

B.B., age 33, had suffered from migraine headaches all her life, but recently they had become worse, often sending her to bed for two or three days. She was a conscientious, hard-working mother, very strict and religious, a perfect housekeeper. Her three small children sometimes made it almost impossible for her to "keep the house up." She had no time for neighbors who did not share her way of life, but was never able to show this dislike for them. She maintained a pleasant facade of neighborliness. When she was able, after some struggle, to stop overemphasizing minor rules of behavior and

53

believed more in God, her need for strong migraine pills diminished. Her religion had somehow simply made her too strict and when she softened her attitude toward other people her headaches lessened.

Headache is the commonest complaint in a doctor's office. At least 80 per cent of all headaches are considered to be psychogenic. The mechanism of psychogenic headaches is clear to anyone who has driven a car in dense, unfamiliar traffic. Psychological tension leads to muscular tension of the muscles of the head and neck. This in turn leads to constriction of the arteries in the head and brain, followed by dilatation and excessive pulsation. Migraine headaches occur in people who are tense, conscientious, of above average intelligence, over-reactive, worrisome, serious, perfectionistic, rigid in morals. Such people are often socially aloof and impersonal, yet they need to be liked by others and are sensitive to criticism. Headaches occur usually when something disturbs or threatens their rigid system of life or beliefs. Such people have had too much of the Law and not enough of the Gospel. A living faith in a loving Christ can relax them and relieve their headaches.

F.L., age 39, came to the doctor because of a full, throbbing feeling in the head, shortness of breath and pain in the chest, all of which the doctor attributed to his high blood pressure. It measured 240/130. History revealed that his wife, her hands full with six children to rear, refused to continue keeping his mother in the home. His mother was an extremely domineering and autocratic, emotionally disturbed old woman. A square look at his problem, faith to arrange more suitable quarters for his aging mother, courage to admit that his wife was right—all combined with the temporary use of appropriate drugs brought his blood pressure down to normal levels and his symptoms subsided.

Hypertension occurs in people of susceptible families who are in a state of suppressed rage or rebellion, who feel hostility they dare not express, who force humor and try to act gay in the face of deep, internal conflicts. Only those who have the faith and courage to bring it all out into the open, look at it, and readjust their lives are likely to succeed in lowering their blood pressure without protracted medical or surgical treatment. Such readjustment is impossible without an abiding conviction that God is good and God is able to redeem man out of all his troubles.

M.L., age 41, a single woman, consulted her physician for relief of a severe, protracted constipation. Stools were hard, small, scybalous, difficult. Cathartics and oil gave only temporary relief. She was a shy, dependent type of personality, living alone with her widowed mother who had protected her daughter too much, too long. Complete reorientation of her personality was impossible, but some improvement in her symptoms occurred when she developed some friendships in her church and learned how to face life more independently.

The colon is a great reflecter of emotions. No wonder the ancients spoke of "bowels of compassion"! Fear, worry, anger, rebelliousness can make for functional diarrhea and ultimately true colitis. Failure of social adjustment, insecurity, overdependence can make for spastic conditions of the colon. When man lives as a perfectly free personality under God and God alone, sharing his freedom with other people, confident and secure in a working Christian fellowship, even his colon benefits from it.

The greatest contribution church members can make for the prevention of psychosomatic illnesses is to build a happy home and foster and promote other happy Christian homes. There is one thing that all neurotic and psychosomatic patients have in common in their histories—an unhappy childhood home. Not all children from unhappy homes develop psychosomatic illness, but all psychosomatic patients have had an unhappy home life. One and all they suffer from life-long emotional insecurity, born of a broken home or of a home spoiled by unloving or immature parents, parents who rejected them or over protected them because of suppressed desires to reject them.

The great need, then, is for happy homes, homes where parents love each other, love and *want* their children, where parents are truthful, kindly, self-controlled, consistent, fair with their children. We need homes where discipline is administered not for the comfort or convenience of the parents but for the benefit of the children. We need homes where discipline is strong enough to impart ethical Christian characteristics of honesty, loyalty, love of truth, unselfishness, courage, diligence, industry, and respect for authority, but where as the children grow into adolescence they are given freedom by degrees to make their own decisions and become independent, adult, mature Christian citizens. In such homes children find emotional security; in short, they find love, which is a child's most fundamental need.

FAITH AND MIRACLES OF HEALING

Not as I will, but as thou wilt.—Matthew 26:39.

Does God actually perform miracles of healing by organic tissue change? Does he ever overrule the laws of nature for an individual case and accomplish supernaturally what cannot be accomplished by ordinary medical treatment? Can he, for example, cure an incurable cancer? Can he take a limb permanently paralyzed by poliomyelitis and make it strong and sound again? Will he take a lung permanently damaged by tuberculosis, scarred with irreversible fibrosis or riddled with cavities and make that lung perfect and whole again? Does he cure leprosy so that not only the Hansen bacillus is gone but the ravages left by the disease in skin, nerve, and muscle are corrected? Under his miraculous touch can a leg bone destroyed by osteomyelitis be restored to X-ray normalcy again and be made to serve the patient as perfectly as his good leg? These questions bring us to the crux of the whole matter of faith healing. Let us try to answer them honestly.

We may start by distinguishing between what God can do and what he does do. For those of us who are evangelical Christians there is no doubt about what God can do. Being almighty and all-knowing, the Creator of this universe and all its laws, he is able to accomplish true miracles of healing if he wants to. Indeed, God would not be God in the full, divine sense of the word, unless he were able to do such things.

The fact that God does accomplish miracles of healing in individual cases seems clear from biblical and religious history. The sober and straightforward men who compiled the Gospel record of Jesus' life on earth, so reliable in other details, could hardly be accused of falsifying the record in reporting his medical miracles. When they report that the blind were made to see, the deaf to hear, the crippled to walk, the lepers to be cleansed I can only accept their record as factual. Sprinkled throughout Christian history since Christ there are also a number of miraculous healings which appear to be bonafide.

An honest medical evaluation of many of the recorded miracles of healing makes one wonder, however, if they were all really as supernatural as they appeared to the primitive medical understanding of earlier centuries. Not to break down the aura of wonder surrounding the miracles of Jesus—but we do have to be honest with ourselves and admit that modern medical science casts a somewhat different light on some of these miracles than they had in the first century. For example, we cannot deny that some of the fevers (e.g., in Peter's mother-in-law or the nobleman's son) Jesus cured miraculously are today cured routinely by antibiotics. Furthermore, we now know that the normal antibody mechanism of the body can be expected to produce spontaneous or natural cures of some very bad fevers by putting the patient through a crisis in which the fever suddenly subsides and the patient improves. In other words, it is possible that the miracle Jesus produced in these cases was more one of superior understanding of the

58

natural processes at work than of supernatural manipulations.

To follow this line of thought further we think of cases thought to be possessed of demons or spirits, such as the obviously epileptic boy described in Mark 9:14-29. The "spirit" which made the boy have convulsions we now know must have been an actual brain disturbance due possibly to birth injury or previous disease or inherited dysfunction of brain tissues. We would not expect Jesus to correct the scientific error in the concept of this disease held by people in his day. But as we look back on this miracle from our vantage point we must call it what it was—a cure of a case of convulsions, possibly epilepsy. We must also reason that since certain cases of infantile convulsions undergo spontaneous remissions or cures when the child reaches a certain age this may well have been the case with the boy Mark describes. While all such cases will show a persistence of abnormal electroencephalograms as long as they live, some of them never have a convulsion after a certain age is reached. In an outward sense, they "outgrow" it. One wonders if the child Jesus cured would not have shown a persistent abnormality in the encephalogram, thus establishing that the cure did not accomplish any actual structural change in the boy's brain tissue but coincided miraculously with the age at which outward convulsions would cease anyway. Thus, again, the miracle would be more one of understanding and prognosis than of actual organic tissue change.

Perhaps all this semi-scientific speculation is beside the point. Even after allowing for the possibility that some cases of miraculous healing have a natural explanation, there still remains a hard core of what would appear to be solid miracles of actual organic tissue change. The man born blind, healed by Jesus, could hardly have had a hysterical or functional blindness. His eyes must have undergone some real change. The lepers Jesus healed must have had a real change, since leprosy is a disease of such obvious, visible pathology that to declare it cured must have required more than a change of ideas in the lepers' minds. Similarly, medical history has recorded miracles of healing which appear to have been substantiated by scientifically proved changes in the patient's body.

Perhaps it does not matter so much whether such miracles have actually occurred or not, so long as we recognize that God can perform miracles if he wants to. Why, then, does not God perform many more miracles of healing than he does?

It seems clear to me that as a regular thing God does not want to produce supernatural miracles of healing and that this is the reason we seldom see any repetitions of the miracles of the New Testament. An out-and-out miracle of healing is, I believe, in God's eyes an inferior method of handling human disease. It is a concession to a generation that is always demanding signs and wonders (John 4:48). If God were to go beyond the laws of nature and produce miracles of healing as a sort of everyday matter here and there throughout the world, we would run into serious difficulties.

Cures wrought easily through an act of simple, childlike faith would undermine the whole system of natural law and order. They would make people disinclined to learn or study that law and order. The world would become a hotbed of spiritual, political favoritism. People who were not healed by faith would start feeling jealous of those who were and wonder why they were so favored in contrast to them. This would do more harm than good. Furthermore, it would tend to remove from the human scene the challenge that compels men to spend endless hours of research and toil to unravel the mysteries of life and death, of disease and health.

There probably are times in history when God has intervened with a frankly miraculous cure of some important individual—important, that is, in his program of redemption. But it would be arrogant of me as a human being to assume that I am so important to God's plan that he must transcend the laws of nature to heal me from my disease now. God may well find it much better for me to endure the disease I have, to cope with it as best I can, to carry it bravely, even to surmount the handicap it brings.

Think for a moment about a girl called Helen Keller. Born blind, deaf, and therefore mute, she was a pathetic case. Could not God have healed her eyes and opened her ears and made her normal like other girls? I am sure he could have done so, and I am sure there were people, relatives and others, who must have asked him in faith to do so. Why, then, did God not so heal Helen Keller? Was it because those who prayed did not have enough faith? Was it because the girl was not a special enough case? No, it was because he found it wisest not to heal her. It proved much better for Helen Keller and for all similarly afflicted people in the world to let her overcome her handicaps. Many greater things were accomplished for Helen Keller and for all mankind because her disabilities were allowed to persist.

What I am trying to say here is that insofar as we can "think God's thoughts after him" we can understand the problem of human disease and suffering enough to know that it is not necessarily best solved by performing a lot of miraculous cures. It may well be a sign of weakness for us to expect a miraculous cure of any illness, except in the most unusual circumstances. The rare circumstances which require a miraculous cure are best left to God. For this reason, in asking for a cure of any incurable or intractable disease condition we should always add, "as thou wilt, O Lord."

Thoughts like these lie behind the suspicion with which many Christian medical workers view widely advertised and publicized faith healing programs. Whether the programs are put on in city auditoriums, churches, or tabernacles, on TV or at grottoes or shrines, the whole idea of publicizing a divine healing program is repulsive to most of us. In the first place, we feel that it is nobody's business but God's to decide when and where healing miracles are necessary. The Spirit of God, like the wind, bloweth where it listeth (John 3:8). We should not try to direct the Spirit of God any more than we try to direct the wind. Furthermore, we feel instinctively that it would be unlike God to heal a few people here and there and leave the great mass of suffering mankind unhealed. I am equally sure that it is God's purpose that we human beings should learn to help one another in our illnesses and that all medical science and medical care are really a part of the service of the kingdom of God on earth. That this work should fall within the orderly framework of natural laws of physiology and pathology seems perfectly in keeping with God's nature.

Practically 100 per cent of the so-called "cures" claimed by faith healers or shrines are on careful medical investigation either emotionally induced illnesses that had no real organic basis in the first place or else they are out-and-out spurious cases of dishonest "cures." Alas, medical history is full of supposedly "cured" diabetics who quit their insulin and died, of supposedly "cured" appendicitis cases that "needed no operation" and later died, of supposedly "cured" cancer patients who went right on and died.

The majestic unfolding of knowledge in human history is no less inspiring in the medical sciences than in theology, philosophy, the arts, or other sciences. In this history a great deal more of the goodness and greatness of God is reflected than in an account of miraculous interruptions of natural law. Basically God is a God of dependable law and order. The history of thought is really the history of man's quest for that law and order.

Let the matter rest with this: We can trust God to heal us from any disease if in his goodness and wisdom he wills to do so. We must trust God implicitly to do what is right. The way in which he wills to heal us is generally the way of applied medical science, a way of understandable law and order, not by sudden, dramatic miracles.

FAITH AND A FAMILY
PREVENTIVE HEALTH PROGRAM

Look to your health if you have it, praise God and value it next to a good conscience—Izaak Walton.

A very fine Christian mother explained to me one day that she did not want her baby immunized against smallpox, diphtheria, whooping cough, tetanus, or polio because her husband felt that God would protect their child against these diseases. She herself did not seem too convinced of the wisdom of this policy, but out of respect for her husband's convictions on this score she complied. I explained how simple, safe, and reliable these immunization procedures were and pushed the matter no further at the time.

Did her husband have a faith in God's protection superior to that of the rest of us? Was his faith bolder and more far-reaching than ours? On the surface it may have appeared so, but on deeper reflection we feel that his was a foolish faith, almost a defiance of the scientific truths that God has graciously inspired mankind to discover and use up to this point in the history of civilization. While it is always somewhat presumptuous for one human being to tell another how to live his life, I finally told this man that he was "way off the track" even in his religious views.

God cannot be expected to protect us from diseases that we can prevent by means readily at our disposal.

When the scientific knowledge of how to prevent certain diseases is once understood by a man it then becomes that man's personal moral responsibility before God to make use of that knowledge. For him to expect God to protect him even though he violates the known rules of health is really tempting God, something which Scripture clearly forbids.

Scientific truth, like all truth, carries with it a certain stewardship responsibility. We are called upon to be stewards of the truth revealed to us. God may forgive and protect a man who unknowingly violates the rules of health because he is misinformed or uninformed, but it is sheer arrogance to expect God to excuse a man from honestly disciplining himself and his family according to the enlightenment that he has.

Medical science today has clearly established beyond any reasonable doubt that in our country immunizations against smallpox, diphtheria, whooping cough, tetanus, polio, and influenza are safe, effective, and necessary for the preservation of personal and public health. Furthermore, effective immunization is available for all those exposed by occupation, contact, or travel to typhoid fever, paratyphoid fever, cholera, tuberculosis, plague, typhus fever, or mumps. To make full use of these immunizations when needed is the duty of every informed Christian. For such a person to fall prey to any of these diseases because of the lack of proper immunizations is really a sin of omission.

There are, of course, some people in our country who do not believe these medical facts. In all fairness, one has to allow them their difference of opinion and patiently hope for the day when the facts will be acceptable to them. More important, there are many areas in the world where these facts are not at all known. The clear duty of the Christian civilization in which we live is to make these facts and their application available to all people in the world as soon as possible. We have a world-wide obligation to be good stewards of these truths. Anything less is pure selfishness.

There are other ways of preventing diseases than by immunization. A summary of these minimum essentials for maximum health is given here for the guidance of parents who want to check up on their family's personal preventive health program. The free society in which we live exerts no military or governmental discipline in applying these principles; the responsibility is clearly up to the individual and his family. Good Christian stewardship of our bodies can be satisfied with nothing less than an up-to-date, intelligent, practical program designed to keep every member of the family at tiptop health as many days a year as possible for as many years as possible.

MINIMUM ESSENTIALS FOR MAXIMUM HEALTH

1. *Intelligent immunizations.* The discussion of this subject given above may be further amplified by consultation with one's personal physician.

2. *Optimum nutrition.* This means a balanced diet every day for every member of the family, from baby to grandma. Such a diet must include adequate protein, minerals, vitamins, energy foods, and fat. Individual needs for diabetics, heart patients, etc., should be care-

67

fully tended to. Recent evidence indicates, for example, that people in coronary families would do well to avoid hard fats, whether of animal or vegetable origin.

3. *Careful cleanliness.* Clean bodies in clean clothes in clean houses stay healthier longer than those where dirt or contaminants are tolerated. Nobody now doubts the importance of this, at least in our society.

4. *Energetic exercise.* Our soft, gadget-loving, labor-saving culture bids fair to forget this important health rule. Honest comparisons of American children with European and other children indicate that our children suffer from too many rides and not enough walking, too much ease and not enough exercise. The schools can help some in overcoming this, but the responsibility in the last analysis falls on the parents.

5. *Rewarding work.* Both mind and body, spirit and bone, soul and sinew are benefited by hard work. Idleness breeds unrest and finally disease.

6. *Relaxing play.* Recreation for the family has become such an accepted watchword in American culture that one hardly has to plead for this point. The important thing to note is that tensions, both personal and interpersonal, are inclined to disappear in the presence of appropriate amounts of relaxing play.

7. *Preventing accidents.* The avoidance of accident-producing pitfalls in the home is a constant duty of parents. One must mention here how important it is to keep medicines and chemicals out of the reach of children.

8. *Satisfactory sex adjustments.* The emotional and physical health of the family depend on husband and wife making a happy adjustment in the marriage re-

lationship and letting the aura of this love pervade the other relationships within the family. Honest help to children in trying to understand the facts of sex as they are needed throughout their development is a minimum essential if this area of life is to be healthy and happy.

9. *Sociable friendships.* The increasing numbers of mentally ill patients would be reduced if every family made it a point to develop some life-long friendships. Friends help absorb the shocks of life and give wonderful help in producing necessary insights into one's own problems.

10. *Faith in God.* A family without God is not only losing out on some important spiritual values, but is actually running a greater health risk than it should. An active, working Christian faith for each member of the family, growing stronger as it associates with other families in a church—this is the greatest health need in America today.

I asked God for strength, that I might achieve;
I was made weak, that I might learn humbly to obey.
I asked for health, that I might do greater things;
I was given infirmity, that I might do better things.
I asked for riches, that I might be happy;
I was given poverty, that I might be wise.
I asked for power, that I might have the praise of men;
I was given weakness, that I might feel the need of God.
I asked for all things, that I might enjoy life
I was given life, that I might enjoy all things.
I got nothing that I asked for, but everything I had hoped for.
I am among men, most richly blessed!

> Author—an unknown Confederate soldier

Type used in this book
Body, 10 on 13 Caledonia
Display, Times Roman
Paper: Spring Grove Antique "R"